best wishes

Daisy and the Isle of Wight Dragon

Martin Simpson

Dedicated to my good friend Ian Forrest

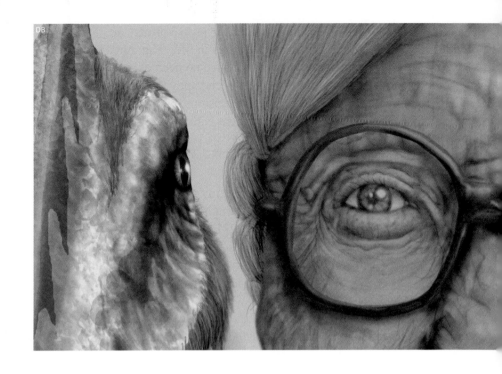

Daisy's Prologue: I am 99 and nearly fossilised.

Call me Daisy. After all, that's my name. I didn't choose it, but a lot of people say it suits me, and I've grown to like it. There weren't any other Daisys at my school or even on the rest of the island where I was born. In fact, in my entire life I have only ever met three other Daisys, and one of those was a pot-bellied pig I saw at a rare breeds park during a school trip.

I am 99 years old this year but I don't look my age, I look like a 95 year old. I do not have a pink rinse because I have no desire to resemble a candy floss. Instead I have let my hair do its own thing and grow wild, grey and wispy like a mass of dusty cobwebs. I have so many wrinkles that my skin resembles an old leather handbag. Wrinkles are a natural part of the ageing process and a symptom of eating well, exercising and spending time in the open air. Those silly, Botox-filled and face-lifted celebrities should spend less time looking in the mirror and get out more in search of lily pads up the Amazon or collecting moulted crab shells on a beach in Dorset. So far, I have visited 23 different countries and can say 'hello, how are you?' in fifteen languages.

Thankfully I do not spend my time on coach trips to Torquay or Benidorm, but have found my own adventures in life. I am not a sheep. I have met many people over the years but have no need of more than five good friends at any one time. Have I been happy? Of course I have been happy in my life, on countless occasions, but more importantly I have been, and still am, content with my lot. I was born a bit different from the norm, or so they say, with an inbuilt curiosity about the natural world and an instinct to collect things that most people would sooner rather not touch, let alone possess.

I digress. This is not a story about my life as such, for that can wait for another time. It's a story about something quite extraordinary that happened to me when I was a small girl living on the Isle of Wight, one of England's hidden treasures. But it's also a tale of fantastical and magical extinct creatures that lived millions of years before we humans, or even the Isle of Wight for that matter, had been invented (if that's the right word, which it isn't.) Somehow, a whole series of events became inter-connected and ultimately changed the course of my life. Some people call that fate, but as I learnt later the only thing that is truly fatal in the world is death. There is death in this story of course, but not in a sad way.

To understand the links in the chain of my story you will have to use your grey matter and cast your mind back to a time on earth known as the 'Age of Reptiles,' which is quite a mind boggling thing to do. If your mind has never been boggled then for goodness sake find something with which to boggle it, other than an iPod or a computer screen. My headmaster, who had very hairy hands and fingers, seemed to be very good at making me think independently and always encouraged me to find things out for myself. 'Thinking outside the box' he called it, but he never told me where the box was or how to get one.

"Don't believe everything you read in books and newspapers and certainly not anything you look up on the internet," he would always tell me. "Mistakes and bunkum, repeated ad infinitum."

My dad, another mind boggler, would have put it this way: "If you can't imagine 120 million years then just think of 60 million years and double it."

I think the best way to continue this story is to hand you over to the author, who will begin in Chapter One with the version my mother read to me, just a year or so after it all happened. From Chapter Two onwards the author will narrate the story in his own words. So if you are ready and concentrating, we can start jumping backwards and forwards in time.

Chapter 1: Daisy's mother takes her daughter back in time

"During the Age of Reptiles there lived a pterosaur called Ginky," began Daisy's mother, Mrs. Sian Morris.

"That's a funny name mummy" interrupted her five year old daughter.

"Yes Daisy that's right but…"

"I thought this story was about me?" the girl retorted.

"Er, not entirely dear, but you are an important part of it."

"What's it about then?" Daisy continued, her eagerness getting the better of her.

"Well, it's about a lot of things really. It's about why things are named the way they are, and it's about the different types of people in this world, some good and some bad."

Daisy's mother had a sudden, strong feeling of déjà vu. She was well aware that her daughter's natural curiosity and enthusiasm were excellent qualities to be encouraged. Her story, however, was only one sentence long, albeit longer than the opening sentence of this book, which Daisy had inadvertently adapted from her favourite bedtime story of all, topping even the tales penned by Jules Verne or Rudyard Kipling: the adventures of Moby Dick. Daisy's mother was getting impatient. One carefully aimed stern glance at her daughter did the trick, an act subtle enough to stem the flow of questions and switch Daisy back to listening mode.

"The Isle of Wight isn't what it used to be. No, one hundred and twenty five million, two thousand and thirteen years ago it looked quite different, felt different and was actually somewhere else all together. Before Jesus Christ, the Egyptians, Neanderthal Man, woolly mammoths and Bob the Builder, this period of time is known as the Age of Reptiles. Scaly, leathery and even feathery-skinned cold blooded 🐾 creatures dominated the land, the sea and even the air. These prehistoric monsters lived right across the globe including a little bit of land we now call the Isle of Wight. In those days it didn't have a name and it wasn't yet an island of course. It was merely part of a larger, ancient land mass joined together with others but in a different way. Our little piece of the jigsaw was much further south and nearer to the Equator, which meant that the climate was almost tropical. It was moist and warm like one of your left over school marmite sandwiches, so warm in fact that the plants and animals were barely recognisable from those of today, unless you visit the national Botanic Gardens at Kew or the local one near Ventnor.

🐾 Footnote: Some might have been warm blooded

Daisy Morris and her collection of bones and stones (DB)

Familiar looking ferns and odd sago palms, the latter resembling punk pineapples, were overshadowed by giant tree-ferns which grew alongside even bigger monkey puzzle or upside down trees. There were hardly any flowering plants other than ones resembling the magnolias popular in today's suburban gardens. Nor were there any grasses, because those had yet to evolve. There wouldn't be any grassy things for another 54 million years, so plant eating dinosaurs had to eat whatever else was available, even if it was tough and chewy.

In the seas there were giant squids and other shellfish, while in the rivers there were crocodiles, sharks, turtles and armoured fishes. The land was the domain of many different kinds of dinosaur, at least thirty that we know about. The sky harboured no bats, and there were probably no owls, budgies or parrots. A few isolated birds were dotted about, I suppose you could call them the early birds, but nothing like the number and variety that exist nowadays. No, apart from insects, the main airborne creatures were the prehistoric reptilian gliders, flappers and darters that came in a variety of ungainly shapes and sizes. These amazing animals included the biggest flying species of all time and ranged in size from a sparrow to a small aeroplane. We call them all pterosaurs, although some people incorrectly use the collective name pterodactyls. That's just what they happened to be called in those corny, crackly old films made before computers, in which the cavemen always wore naff mammoth-skin underpants and grunted a great deal. No, the proper name is pterosaurs, which means winged lizards.

125 million years BC was the start of another year in pterosaur history. One pterosaur family in particular was about to get somewhat larger, because one of the eggs which had been carefully nurtured for four weeks in the nest was about to reveal its reptilian contents. The egg was only the size of a grape, that is to say a grape about the size of a pterosaur egg. Gradually the soft shell split like crazy paving and a tiny baby pterosaur slowly and clumsily scrambled out. It was a female pterosaur that would grow up to be about the size of a modern day wood pigeon.

As the saurian fledgling struggled to stand up straight and take in her surroundings, her parents and other onlookers couldn't help noticing a distinctive marking on the back of her neck, something a palaeobotanist would instantly recognise as being the shape of a particular fossil plant.

'What's my name?' the tiny pterosaur blurted.

This outburst took everyone by surprise, but there were more questions to come.

'What are those things over there?' she boldly asked her mother, pointing first to a flock of larger pterosaurs in the middle distance and then to a group of long necked dinosaurs in the valley beyond.

Before anyone could muster an answer, the infant creature was mentally surveying the landscape around her and the myriad of animals it contained. The sea in the far distance was teeming with long and short necked aquatic monsters familiar to us as plesiosaurs and ichthyosaurs, and lots of fish. Her natural curiosity was obvious for all to see. Over the next few weeks she would bombard her parents with countless questions. For now they only told her what she needed to know, which wasn't much.

The baby pterosaur enters the world (DB)

'Those creatures are different from us' her mother began, breaking the silence with a tone that commanded immediate attention. 'Those dinosaurs and sea creatures keep to their own kind in their own homes and so do we. That way we do not bother each other. Our home is the low coastal forest and the sky above, and all of our food can be found there. If you learn how to catch your own meals and keep safe while you're doing it, you'll be more than happy amongst your own kind.'

The baby's instincts were already telling her to keep well out of the way of the other animals. It was everyone for themselves, eat or be eaten!

'There are many different types of pterosaur around us. Look up high and you can see those enormous gliding ones with the large crests on their heads.'

'But why are we so much smaller than them?' the baby asked her mother. She was beginning to realise that all these differences were important, but wouldn't know just how important until many years later.

'This is as big as we get,' demonstrated her mother, spreading out a pair of old wings stretched like chamois leather over the fragile frame of her long skinny fingers. 'But it means we are much more agile than our rivals, enabling us to dart about quickly in times of danger.'

'But why are we.....?'

Before the inquisitive hatchling could finish her sentence her mother abruptly ended the conversation. 'That's just the way things are.'

'Your name? You wanted to know your name?' The baby's father had remained quiet for all this time but now it was his turn to speak. 'Look into that puddle of water, at your own image. Take a good look at yourself. You are small and gangly. Your toothless beak is pointed and you have a special crest above your head. You are just like all of us gathered here now, but in one small way you are different, in fact unique.'

The baby pterosaur struggled to see the details of her tiny frame in the muddy puddle, failing to spot the special difference her father had just mentioned.

'There is a mark in the fur on the back of your neck that is visible to everyone but you. It immediately reminded your mother and I of the leaf of a rare plant in the valley known as the Ginkgo 🍃 so we are going to call you Ginky.'

🍃 Ginkgo is a fossil plant with very distinctive leaves

Ginky was happy with her name and was feeling quite content being a pterosaur, albeit a small one. They definitely weren't the prettiest creatures in the world, their awkward bodies designed purely for lifestyle and not for winning beauty contests. But amongst them, apparently, she was unique."

~

Daisy's note: It was about this point in the story that I remember interrupting my mother and pointing out some obvious discrepancies that had crossed my mind. Not only couldn't pterosaurs speak of course, but also the creatures wouldn't have had modern names. In her defence, Mum pointed out that there was no such thing as a pterosaur/English-English/pterosaur dictionary so if I wanted to hear the rest of the story I would just have to like it or lump it. Either that or the pterosaurs would simply screech like barn owls and have silly cartoon names like 'Little Foot,' 'Starflower' or 'Stumpy.' She also explained to me what a smart alec was.

Ginky had an unusual marking on her neck which resembled the leaf of a Ginkgo plant. This meant she always stood out from the crowd.

A Ginkgo leaf

 A Ginky is also a computer nerd, apparently

Chapter 2: In which the author is the narrator and we go back to the future

In 2001 it was the beginning of a new millennium, the start of another one thousand years of human history (as opposed to prehistory.) Obviously there never was a year 0, but it was two thousand years or thereabouts since the birth of a man called Jesus (Christ), a man who literally changed time. The years before Christ are counted back in years BC, so 100 years BC is earlier than 50BC. After this point the years progress forwards and are given the initials AD, short for Anno Domini, which means the year of our Lord. In reality, however, hardly anyone bothers to use them.

It was on one particularly windy winter's day in 2001 AD at the start of this new millennium that Mr. and Mrs. Morris found themselves in the maternity ward of their local, one and only hospital on the Isle of Wight. They were looking at an ultrasound scan of their fourth child, due to be born that September, the seventh month of the year.

"Well, if the baby's a girl what are we going to call her?" asked Mr. Morris, changing the mood of silent contemplation to one of more practical matters. The Morrises had always agreed that their daughters would be named after flowers, so the new arrival would join her sisters Poppy and Lily in the floral household.

"How about Daisy?" suggested Mrs. Morris, turning her gaze to a tall vase next to a plate containing the remains of the matron's recent lunch.

Mr. Morris followed his wife's glance. "Well it's better than Daffodil or Carnation, or even Cabbage come to that!" he mused, wondering why the head nurse hadn't eaten all of her greens.

The Morris clan also included a solitary boy called Riann, who was named after his grandfather Riann thanks to a long family tradition. One vintage Riann Morris was a soldier who had fought in the First World War, although in those days it came to be known as the Great War. Afterwards he and many of his fellow soldiers thought that this name was particularly inappropriate for any war, let alone that one.

"Alright" agreed Mr. Morris, "Daisy she shall be."

RB

Now it's the ninth

Chapter 3: In which we learn about the Isle of Wight and the Fossil Man

For anyone who doesn't know, the Isle of Wight is a small island tucked away off the southern coast of England 75 miles away from London. It is only 23 miles wide and 16 miles tall, small enough to get to know but big enough not to feel claustrophobic about. The land is shaped roughly like a diamond or lozenge, but the older inhabitants thought it looked like a flounder, a type of flatfish. These days not many people would recognise a flounder in a supermarket, nor any fish that wasn't shaped like a finger for that matter, so the diamond comparison seems as good as any.

People born on the Isle of Wight are known as 'caulkheads,' pronounced cork heads, because caulking a boat was something boat builders did to make their vessels watertight in the days long before things were made of plastic or fibreglass. The caulk was a mixture of cotton fibres and oakum (hemp fibre soaked in pine tar). Some say the caulk heads will float to the surface if the Island ever finally sinks beneath the waves. Whatever the story, the Isle of Wight is famous for boats of all kinds. Just to get there you have to use catamarans, hydrofoils and even hovercraft, which is all part of the excitement of paying a visit. Cars are transported from the mainland by roll-on ferries resembling giant metal boxfish. Boats are a local way of life, especially around the town of Cowes where each August the yachties gather in their thousands to show off their vessels, deck shoes and anoraks.

Wight Island is also famous on account of some of the important people who once lived there, including the bearded poet Tennyson and the non-bearded monarch Queen Victoria. Not quite as well known is the fact that garlic is grown on the downs, all the rage in posh restaurants where gastronomes crave thin blood and smelly breath. But enough of all these culinary and historical digressions, what the Island is really famous for, I mean really world famous for, is **DINOSAURS!**

In 2001 the Isle of Wight was becoming justifiably proud of its dinosaurs and other fossils excavated from the soft clays and sandstones exposed along its coastal cliffs. These rocky relics constantly erode out of a shrinking island and are the petrified bones and shells of once living creatures from the time of Ginky the pterosaur. A brand spanking new museum had recently been built in the tourist town of Sandown, famous for its long sandy beaches stretching for miles in front of a backdrop of the glorious red and white cliffs, which for some reason had been named Redcliff and Whitecliff respectively.

The Isle of Wight 125 million years ago as drawn by palaeo-artist Mark Witton

The glistening metal museum was full of fossils, some of them collected by tourists, amateurs and even famous geologists from the days of Queen Victoria. Large spiral shell fossils, some as big as tractor tyres, lined the walls. In between them were placed life-sized models so the visitors could imagine what the animals might once have looked like. Examples of many other shells, lobsters, bits of crocodiles and plants were arranged neatly in glass cabinets accompanied by labels detailing their unpronounceable Latin names. But pride of place went to the fossilised bones belonging to the dinosaurs. Mostly these were plant eaters like the spiky-thumbed Iguanodon, impressive enough on their own, but the most exciting exhibit by far was the almost complete skeleton of a carnivorous theropod monster labelled Neovenator. Its black and shiny mineralised bones were assembled together in an impressive upright pose. Although smaller than a T-rex, measuring some 7 metres long from head to toe, this meat-eating prehistoric caulkhead with its unfamiliar name was still scary enough to impress visiting children and parents alike.

However, despite the modern architecture and all the fossilised paraphernalia it contained, there was something lacking in this museum; something just wasn't quite right. For all the money the place cost to build, the sum of all the parts didn't generate that special atmosphere its amazing contents deserved.

Meanwhile, on the opposite side of the diamond shaped island, set in the remote downland countryside not far from the crumbling clay undercliffs, was another, smaller and quite different museum. This was run by one man, known to most Isle of Wighters and tourists as the Fossil Man. His museum consisted of a small collection of rented barns in an old dairy farm, parts of which dated back to the seventeenth century. Birds and beetles were frequent uninvited guests at the museum, and you had to be careful where you stood and what you stood in. The Fossil Man jokingly used to warn his visitors that the floor was so dirty the cockroaches walked round on stilts. Conditions weren't ideal, the barns were draughty, cold and damp, but they would serve as a temporary base until he found the perfect site of his own.

Due to his habit of selling fossilised crocodile droppings to tourists in a local pub, the Fossil Man had been given the nickname Croc which, if you think about it, could have been worse. A small purpose built glass cabinet on the bar once contained splendid examples of these rather unusual prehistoric souvenirs, next to which was a hand written card that read 'fossilised poo....if you wish to buy one please leave a deposit.'

On this particular day a school party was huddled on the floor and was about to be addressed by Croc the Fossil Man, surrounded by his collection of bones, teeth, shells, claws and skulls.

"Welcome to the museum everyone, my name is Croc but you can call me Biro if you like, that's my pen name."

This was how the Fossil Man liked to start every talk to every school group. What made him laugh (inside) was the fact that none of the schoolchildren ever got his jokes. One thing was certain though, they couldn't fail to appreciate his enthusiasm.

"Alright, I will need a volunteer please" he said hopefully, scanning the eager faces in front of him. None of the children were quite at the age to have learned never to volunteer for anything in life, so there was no shortage of guinea pigs. He quickly made his choice.

"Okay, the young lady in the blue hat, would you like to come forward please?" The girl obligingly stood up and peeled away from the remaining group of blue-hatted pupils.

"What is your name please?" the Fossil Man asked, to which the girl politely replied 'Chelsea'. "Oh that's a nice name, is it your father's favourite football team or was it the place where he met your mother?"

No, it turned out that Chelsea's parents had named their daughter after a popular television celebrity who was very pretty and had extremely white teeth, hair extensions and an orange face. On another occasion the reply had been 'Amy', which the Fossil Man knew to mean 'beloved' and, as it happened that time, so did Amy. There had often been an Emily, a name he knew meant 'hard working' because that was the precise name he had chosen for his own daughter. Whether she was or not was too early to say. His original idea was to give his planned six daughters geological names like Coral, Crystal, Ruby, Jade or Amber, but things don't always go to plan. In the end he settled for Emily, or Emily 5 as she became known at school some years later, when it transpired that four other sets of parents had come up with the same idea.

Addressing the group sitting in front of Chelsea, the self-styled curator of the off-beat museum asked the children how many of them actually knew the meaning of their own names. This time it was about a quarter, it usually was. But one particular volunteer took him by surprise. The name Alakesha had the Fossil Man genuinely puzzled.

"And what does Alakesha mean, I've never heard of that one before?"

"It doesn't mean anything" replied Alakesha. "It's just that when my mother asked my big sister what she would like her new baby to be called, that was the name she made up on the spot."

This struck a chord with the fossiler, who appreciated rarity of any kind.

During every talk the Fossil Man showed his audience a selection of fossils to help him relay his story. Touching the dinosaur droppings or coprolites always went down well with unsuspecting volunteers, who were just beginning to realise the consequences of putting their hands up in the first place. At the end of each session there was always time for questions from the audience, the most usual of which were:

What is your favourite dinosaur?..."Iguanodon with its pointed thumbs"
What is your best find?.............."always a difficult one to answer"
How much are they worth?..........(usually asked by the more materialistic pupils who went on to become bank managers and estate agents)
Why did the dinosaurs become extinct?.................

This last question was always met with a different answer because the theories of extinction kept changing as scientists discovered more about dinosaurs and their world. The Fossil Man always wanted to find time to write books about dinosaurs but was constantly put off by the fact that most of them have the same ending: the dinosaurs always snuff it.

On a wall in the museum was a list of schoolchildren's ideas as to why these prehistoric creatures became extinct: they got too big, mice ate their eggs, it got too hot, it got too cold and their private parts fell off, they smoked too much or they couldn't fit on Noah's Ark.

As it happened, scientists now know that some dinosaurs had feathers and didn't become extinct after all, they simply evolved into birds. The funny comments were the sort of things you would expect from the minds of eleven year old children, but every now and then a more thought-provoking question would catch the Fossil Man by surprise.

"How do you know dinosaurs all had those names?" asked a boy called Sammy.

"Well, that is just what we call them in our own language," came the reply. "Lots of dinosaur names end in 'saurus,' which means lizard, and some are named after unusual features of their bodies, the place where they were found or even the person who found them. Some names sound weird and others are just plain daft. But for every new dinosaur we name there must be an actual specimen in a museum available for study."

Sammy looked bemused. "Can't you just sell it?"

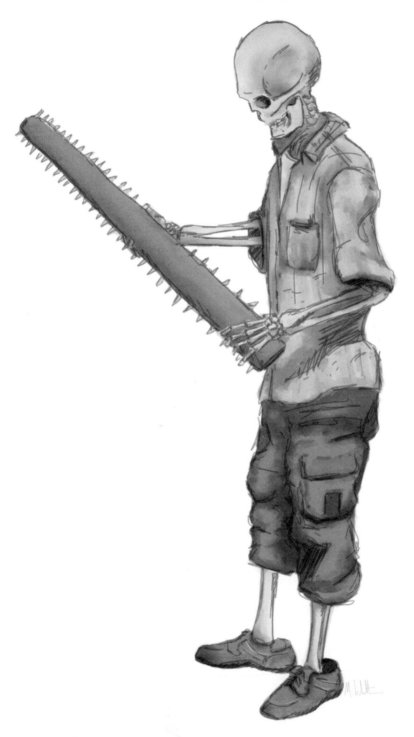

The Fossil Man couldn't help wondering if his nickname gave people the impression that he was very old.

"Well you can, but sometimes they are so rare that their value is measured not in cash but in scientific terms. These rarities really belong in a national museum."

When he was Sammy's age the Fossil Man had become fascinated with fossils and always wanted to open his very own museum. Since then he had collected over 50,000 fossils in 30 years, a collection so huge it once completely filled every room of his suburban maisonette. He was getting desperate to put on a proper public display. For the time being some of them were dotted around this rented huddle of farmyard barns, complete with a horse field for a car park. Inside it was bitterly cold in the winter and the roof always leaked when it rained. But it would do for now.

Another panorama as imagined by Louis, aged 8 from Lancing

Chapter 4: In which we briefly go back in time again and split an infinitive

Ginky the pterosaur had been out feeding and was now back home safely, perched on a low cliff alongside her mother and two brothers. She was now five years old. She had flown over the valley and along the coast thousands of times already and knew her territory inside out.

"One day I will be able to fly much further away and explore the coastal lagoons where the seas are much clearer and shallower. They are full of weird and wonderful creatures, so I'm told," she said out loud to no-one in particular.

Her mother suddenly stopped preening herself and, for the first time in Ginky's short life, spoke directly to her daughter in a colder, more serious tone of voice. She seemed to take an age to deliver her well chosen words.

"When you are older and have brought up a family of your own, only then can you think of venturing beyond the boundaries of our world. You have a duty to teach your future children all the things you have learned from me. But until then you must try and keep safe for all our sakes."

"But why can't I go off now and have some fun for a change?"

The young pterosaur avoided her mother's gaze because she realised straight away that this was one question that should never have been asked. She had dropped a major clanger and never asked it again.

Ichthyosaur and Ammonites by Thomas, aged 10 from Painswick

Millions of years ago the sea was full of giant ammonites, ichthyosaurs, solicitors and other slimy creatures

Daisy's vision of her Isle of Wight Dragon (DB)

Chapter 5: In which the Loch Ness Monster makes an appearance for some strange reason

Back on the present day Isle of Wight, the Fossil Man was halfway through a tour of his half-finished museum. Every visitor embarked on a twenty minute guided tour, whether they wanted one or not. Afterwards, most were glad they had.

"Okay folks, here we have my collection of huge fossilised shells that we call ammonites, once home to giant, squid-like creatures that propelled themselves backwards in the sea, trying to escape from Sir David Attenborough." He paused briefly to let the small crowd gaze upon the rows of local ammonites collected over many years, and for the information to sink in.

"Does anyone know what might have had a mouth big enough to eat one of these shellfish?" At this point, some wag in the audience would obligingly exclaim 'my mother in law!' or something similar, but luckily instead a young boy broke the silence by providing the Fossil Man with the prompt he was looking for.

"A plesiosaurus" the child spouted confidently.

"Very good. That is one specific kind of underwater giant marine reptile of course, but there were several others. Some people believe that plesiosauruses are still alive today living in the murky waters of Loch Ness in Scotland."

Personally, the Fossil Man did not think that Nessie had ever lived, finding it hard to accept the existence of something he could neither see in the wild nor touch in a museum, zoo or aquarium. On the other hand, he didn't mind that there were some people who really did believe in the enigmatic creature. After all, he informed his audience, despite surviving uncaptured and unseen in detail for all these years, the Loch Ness Monster had been given the dubious honour of being awarded a proper scientific name by real scientists with real beards, even though there wasn't a single live, dead or stuffed museum specimen on which to attach a label. It was called *Nessiteras rhombopteryx.*

Sometimes the intrepid explorer lurking within the Fossil Man wondered whether he should go on a life changing expedition to Scotland to bag a real specimen of Nessie, becoming rich and famous in the process. Then he could finance his own museum. But then again he liked the Isle of Wight too much and was never really driven by money. You only had to look at his jacket, held together with a safety pin, to realise that. No, there were still too many undiscovered fossils on his own patch on the Isle of Wight.

This is an anagram of 'monster hoax by Sir Peter S'

Asked by his daughter if he was rich or famous, he wondered which she thought more important.

"Why, being rich of course" was her first response, but after a short pause she seemed to change her mind. "No, being famous actually....or maybe a bit of both!"

"Well I'm not very rich yet but I am world famous in Blackgang on the Isle of Wight, so is that good enough for you?"

Emily thought it probably was.

Some of the Fossil Man's audience were familiar with other prehistoric sea reptiles including ichthyosaurs and pliosaurs, but not mosasaurs. So he pointed to a life sized model of one, suspended from the old wooden beams in the roof of the barn.

"Look!" he exclaimed excitedly, "You've all heard of the Loch Ness Monster, which does NOT exist, and no-one has heard of the poor old Mosasaurus, which definitely DID!"

The tourists gazed in awe at the twenty feet long skeletal creature hanging above them like a bony, old fashioned clothes airer. It sported flippers and a short neck, and an impressive set of conical teeth that could easily have made short work of a giant ammonite shell. It also had an unusual addition which only a minority of onlookers spotted - a toy, yellow Teletubby stuck between its jaws.

As they continued their tour, the exuberant guide went on to recount the legendary tale of the famous fossil woman who lived in Dorset two hundred years ago, Miss Mary Anning. She notably found an impressive specimen of the dolphin-like ichthyosaurus when she was only twelve years old. Later she topped that discovery with the very first complete plesiosaurus and the very first British pterosaur. Some people had vaguely heard of Mary Anning of course, but others were more familiar with the tongue twisting ditty that was said to have been inspired by her life:

'She sells sea shells on the sea shore;
The shells that she sells are sea shells, I'm sure.'

Mary became truly world famous, not only because of her many fossil discoveries but also because she was a woman, and an unusual woman at that. Pointing to a copy of the portrait of Miss Anning blue-tacked to the wall he was leaning on, the Fossil Man couldn't help but point out that she was no Cheryl Cole in the looks department. "Still" he contemplated, "You never get everything in life!"

'Nessie,' the Loch Ness Monster: plesiosaurus or a figment of our imagination?

Legend has it that Mary Anning was struck by lightning as a baby and was transformed into the 'Fossil Woman' (DB)

There have been many dreadful poems written about Mary Anning, so here is another one.

> *Fossil Mary, quite contrary,*
> *What sea shells do you sell?*
> *"Ammonites and belemnites…*
> *But coprolites go down quite well!"*
>
> *Despite the cash, despite the fame,*
> *Why do you look so glum?*
> *Failed romances? All male chances?*
> *Ne'er mind, your time and place will come.*

Mary Anning's Motorway Poem (I wrote it on the M42)

Chapter 6: In which we go back in time for a final visit

Ginky the pterosaur had lived a long life for a flying reptile, thus far forty years. In animal terms this isn't as long as the average lifespan of a tortoise or a parrot, but significantly more than that of a mayfly, which only lasts for a paltry 24 hours. She had raised twenty 'chicks' of her own and had looked after them well, bringing them up in the same way she had been taught so expertly in turn.

The time she was always yearning for had come late in her life. Breaking the safety barrier, she had flown confidently and fearlessly beyond the coastal mountains and invaded the territory of her distant reptilian cousins, the huge long necked dinosaurs. She was a stranger to stress and was enjoying her life to the full: her offspring had flown the nest, her mate had long since passed away and she could concentrate on her own feelings and ambitions. This particular day in our story she was flying high over the most dangerous, stupidly large predators around, the Neovenators. She was living her dream while enjoying the wisdom and experience of old age. More importantly she was LIVING.

This time Ginky did not return to her home and was never seen again by any of her own kind.

I am not a number, I am a free Lower Cretaceous azhdarchoid pterosaur (DB)

Chapter 7: *A longer one this time, making up for chapters 2, 4 and 6*

One spring day in the school holidays, Daisy Morris and her family decided to venture out on one of their periodic fossil hunting expeditions. Daisy had the collector's instinct, an in-built fascination for dead animals of all kinds. Already, aged 5, she had gathered together quite an impressive display of fossilised shells and bits of real birds' skeletons picked up in the fields near the family cottage. While other girls her age were playing with dolls' houses, toy ponies or Barbies, Daisy's bedroom was beginning to resemble a small museum of natural history. A dried bat in a jam jar, chocolate boxes full of snail shells, birds' feathers, the skull of a fox, ammonites from the cliff, various unknown teeth: these were just a few of her prized possessions stored under her bed or placed carefully on every available shelf. She told her mother she might one day put the whole collection on show in the garden shed and charge her friends fifty pence admission.

On the Isle of Wight, the worse the weather the better the prospects for fossil collecting. A south-westerly gale had passed through the day before, so the sea was still quite rough and the waves of the morning tide had washed right over the soft blue clay at the foot of the cliff. Being the highest of all, the spring tides were by far the best for beach combers, metal detectorists and fossil hunters alike, for they could strip away tons of shingle and scour out hidden treasures usually covered up in the summer months. A dark line in the clay marked the highest reach of the tide, but by now the sea was retreating pretty fast and there was no time to lose. The Morrises made their way to the beach with eager anticipation. Their way down was a rambling path following the route of a steep natural gorge cut through the clay and shale by a fast running stream. These gorges or chasms were known locally as chines, and this one was called Shepherd's Chine. The story went that long ago a shepherd had diverted the course of the stream to the beach by cutting a channel through the soft rock, and thus it became Shepherd's Chine, the only access to the beach for miles. As they descended deeper into the earth's crust our intrepid hunters passed by the distinctive parallel bands of soft sedimentary rocks scoured clean by the orange stream. They had been down this muddy path many times.

The orange colour is caused by the iron derived from the rocks

Before too long they arrived on the beach, piled high with glistening mounds of smooth flint pebbles. That day, like most days outside the tourist season, the bay was deserted as far as the eye could see, except for one solitary figure some way off to the east. Soon Daisy could make out the outline of a bearded old man collecting driftwood and the odd fishing buoy stranded by the receding tide. The man was known to many people, but not to the Morrisses, as Scratcher, and although he dressed like a scarecrow he apparently had a heart of gold. Seeing Daisy approaching, Scratcher drew attention to himself by picking up a loose flip flop from a pile of flotsam. "Whoever lost this will be hopping mad, har har!" he shouted at her.

Daisy said nothing.

"You looking for *farsils* or old coins, Missy? I collects pirate treasure yer see, especially silver pieces of eight, and Roman coins too. If you ever comes across a coin with 300BC written on it, I'll pay you a thousand pounds for it, maybe more."

Scratcher's ruddy face broke out into large grin which revealed more gaps than teeth. His jokes went down like a wet pair of pants but that didn't seem to bother him in the slightest. By this time Daisy's mother had caught up with her daughter.

"Right I'm off," the beachcomber blurted, "time and tide wait for no man as they say in Japan hahar! In any case, I'm getting the beginnings of a cold so I'm going to go straight to bed with a hot Bovril and a fisherman's friend."

After he had wandered well out of earshot, Daisy turned to her mother and spoke her mind.

"Mummy that man was very funny."

"Yes dear" her mother replied quickly, "funny peculiar." As she turned to take another look at the eccentric loner he stopped for a while, picked some food particles out of his remaining teeth and belched so loudly he dispersed all of the seagulls in the vicinity.

Daisy wasted no more time and was soon adding to her collection of natural curiosities. Fossilised limestone oysters the size of tea plates, empty mermaid's purses, clusters of whelk's eggs and glistening nuggets of fool's gold were all carefully placed in a blue plastic bucket normally reserved for making sandcastles in the summer holidays. Then something unusual attracted Daisy's attention.

Scratcher earned his nickname from his unique method of searching for treasures with a big stick, or possibly because he sometimes used it to scratch his buttocks

"Mummy, what's this?" she called out loudly, trying to make herself heard above the noise of the crashing waves dragging the pebbles back towards the sea as if trying to reclaim them for some obsessed underwater collector.

"What is it Daisy, what have you found?" replied an eager Mrs. Morris, keen to foster her daughter's enthusiasm. She marched across the shingle towards the edge of a landslipped portion of the main cliff, two steps forward and one down as the pebbles gave way beneath her wellies. Daisy was pointing at a large chunk of clay known to everyone on the Isle of Wight as 'blue slipper.' One Island town, Ventnor, was entirely built on this infamous, glutinous stratum and was now sliding towards the sea at an alarming rate, alarming that is if you happened to live there.

"Oh Daisy, it looks like fossil wood, like tiny branches or twigs made of lignite or sea coal" was Mrs. Morris's initial appraisal. Getting closer and looking harder she quickly realised the true significance of her daughter's find.

"No wait, look, they're fossilised bones, shaped just like your real bird skeleton at home. Only see how they're all shiny and black."

By now the whole family had gathered around the rocky outcrop and were busily searching the surrounding area for more pieces of Daisy's mysterious fossil. Soon, satisfying themselves there were no more fragments to be found, Daisy, Lily, Poppy and Riann carefully wrapped the tiny perfect bones in anything that came to hand: bits of tissue, newspaper and even Daisy's hanky, monogrammed with a flowery 'D.' The family, complete with their new addition, carried on searching until they reached the headland at Fishing Cove before turning around to begin their long march back to the car. Although they were not really sure what they had found, they were certain in their minds that it was something out of the ordinary, something quite different to anything they had seen on previous expeditions. Something definitely worth getting excited about.

The following day the Morrises took their fossils to the new, state of the art county dinosaur museum at Sandown, where they hoped to see the new curator, a renowned foreign expert on fossil bones. Mr. Morris thought he would save the best until last, so he offered up his daughter's oyster shells and crystals to start the ball rolling.

"We found all these at Shepherd's Chine after yesterday's high tide" he explained to the lady receptionist, handing the priceless family treasures over the counter for inspection. The lady had an expression of slight disapproval, as if there were a bad smell under her nose.

"Mummy, what's this?" (RB)

"Mmm" she responded with an unenthusiastic air. "The curator is very busy but I will see if he can spare a moment. Wait here, I shan't be two minutes."

"One, two.." counted Daisy mentally, but to no avail.

Mr. Morris felt slightly underwhelmed but remained hopeful of a better response from the museum's very own fossil expert. However, things deteriorated not two but sixteen minutes later with the arrival of a rather stern looking middle aged man who glanced quickly and dismissively at the family's offerings.

"We see a lot of zees sort of thing here" he said abruptly in a rather strange accent Mr. Morris didn't recognise, stroking his greying beard vigorously.

"Zey are very common shells from the shores around the Island. Do you have anything else you wish me to look at?"

"Er no, that's it I'm afraid" replied Mr. Morris without hesitation. "Thank you for your time Mr......"

"Dr..... it's DR, Tito Shuban" the curator stressed.

Mr. Morris hurriedly packed away the fossils into a Tesco carrier bag, rounded up his bemused family and ushered them through the revolving door and out into the gravel car park.

"But Dad what about the...?"

"It's okay Daisy, I know just the place to go."

In the car Daisy turned to her mother and broke the silence of the journey.

"That man was funny" she said.

"He didn't make me laugh much" interrupted Mr. Morris who had overheard his daughter's remark above the noise of the engine.

"I meant funny peculiar."

It turned out that Dr. Shuban, regarded as an expert in fossil bones by some academics but not others, had only recently come to the museum to replace a previous, retired curator. He was not particularly renowned for his charm or wit.

There are two types of people in this world: collectors and normal people

Chapter 8: Later that week

"What do you think of these small fossil bones?" Mr. Morris asked.

Daisy and her family had arrived this time at the Fossil Man's museum, not all that far from the beach and the original source of their new discovery. Disappointingly, the owner himself was not there that day, so they showed the treasures instead to a man at the counter. He introduced himself as Mark Sciopi, a part time volunteer with particularly greasy hair and a thick metal bar through his nose. Sciopi got out a small hand lens from one of the many pockets in his fisherman's jacket and perused the bones intently. Mr. Morris watched closely, but felt slightly uneasy about showing something potentially so important to an assistant he knew nothing about. Sciopi peered through his spyglass for an age, made the necessary gestures and then took a deep breath.

"Yerrrrrrrrrrrs well" he sighed, "we come across a lot of these horror stories I'm afraid. This is only part of the original fossil, so the rest must have been lost. I am fairly confident it belongs to some sort of small dinosaur, something like the tiny plant-eating types we get from time to time in the cliffs round here."

Mr. Morris had already heard enough. Here we go again, he thought to himself, deciding what to do next.

"You could leave it here with us at the museum, but you should also be aware that fossils like these really belong to the landowners who own the cliffs down to the high tide mark" continued the assistant, who by now was starting to get on Mr. Morris's nerves.

Sensing he wasn't really getting anywhere in the proceedings, the expert began fidgeting noticeably and tried changing tack. He looked again at the specimen temporarily in his care, the look of a book dealer who had just spotted a rare first edition in a charity shop.

"Failing that we could simply buy the fossil from you, for say £50, on the understanding that it just might be something interesting."

Mr. Morris looked into the man's eyes. He didn't trust him any further than a midget could throw a dinosaur, so he simply made his excuses, packed up the bones as hurriedly as he could, and left.

"I really don't understand these people" Mr. Morris confided to his wife back at their cottage over a cup of tea in front of their open fire. "For starters they show no interest at all and then they try and tell us we shouldn't have it in the first place. If it's not that exciting why would someone offer us money? This is all getting ridiculous, what shall we do now?"

Mrs. Morris was just as perplexed as her husband over the behaviour of so called experts, but suggested a solution. "Let's track down this Fossil Man himself and see what he thinks. We'll ring first and make sure he's there, then see what he makes of it all."

As it happened, the next day the Morrises were told via the Island grapevine that the fossil collector they sought could be found at a spot called Whale Chine, where he was searching for giant ammonites. They arrived to find his empty car parked next to an ice cream van rocking slightly in the wind, so they decided to wait.

"Who fancies a 99 then?" Mr. Morris asked his passengers. "Stay inside in the warm while I nip out and order them."

He knocked on the window of the semi dilapidated van, which had been sealed tight to keep out the ever increasing south-westerly breeze. Gradually a glass door slid open and a robust blonde lady poked her head out slowly, like a pet tortoise searching for its lettuce.

"Can we have five medium 99's please, we're waiting for the Fossil Man?"

"Coming right up" she responded, "only it's from a proper scoop and not that sloppy rubbish you realise. I only sell REAL ice cream."

Seeing the lady piling three generous scoops on each cone, Mr. Morris couldn't help but wonder how big the large ones would have been. Ramming a flake in each teetering masterpiece, the vendor carefully handed every one through the gap and grabbed the proffered ten pound note quickly before it blew away.

"Ah yes, Croc the Fossil Man, he'll be up soon because the tide will be coming back in and he usually likes to have a cuppa before I leave at 4." She smiled to reveal an impressive set of overly large, yellowish teeth partially smeared with red lipstick. "Here's your change darling."

~

A wry smile spread across the Fossil Man's face, slightly reddened like Noddy's from years of beachcombing on windy beaches. He had joined the Morrises in their car with his hot dog and tea which, after four hours on the beach, tasted far better than they should have done.

"Yes.... these are definitely fossil bones and could only be part of a small dinosaur of some kind, a tiny adult or maybe a baby of something slightly bigger." He went on, cradling his hot polystyrene cup: "We need to show them to another expert, but this time someone who is a real specialist in reptile fossils, someone who spends a lot of time studying just these particular bones."

The Fossil Man had already apologised for the unhelpful actions of the temporary assistant at his museum, someone he had employed in good faith but had turned out to be a bit of a disappointment.

"I'm afraid the last straw was when he identified a mystery object brought in by a visitor as a skullcap of a meat-eating dinosaur, when in reality it turned out to be a piece of coconut shell washed up on the beach. Needless to say" he sighed, "I will be dispensing with his services from now on."

"He wasn't a complete idiot though, Croc" Mr. Morris replied reassuringly.

"How so?" said the avid collector, finishing off his double hotdog laced with far too much English mustard.

"Well I noticed he had a front tooth missing!"

The Fossil Man was a specialist himself but only in fossilised lobsters and ammonites, he explained, and this animal was patently neither of those. Having collected over 50,000 individual items in thirty years, he knew a little about a lot of different Isle of Wight fossils, but insisted that they needed someone who knew even more than him. "After all," he quipped, "that's what a specialist is, someone who learns more and more about less and less." It was a joke of sorts, but everyone was too excited to notice. At last, Mr. Morris thought, someone who isn't patronising and doesn't want to take away our fossil under false pretenses.

It wasn't long before news spread of Daisy's important find. Within days the family had received a glut of letters, phone calls and emails probing for more information and in several cases offering to buy the specimen outright. One website owner even posted a picture and claimed to have found it himself!

"That assistant must have taken a photograph on his mobile phone" Mr. Morris deduced. "I'll give Croc a ring to see what he makes of it all."

"Don't panic!" came the reassuring reply. "This fossil is not worth millions of pounds but it is potentially very important for palaeontology, possibly a new species altogether. It's only to be expected that others would come out of the woodwork and be envious of your find. They just want it for themselves, for greed, fame or glory."

"But some of them are saying we shouldn't have it at all, that it doesn't belong to us and that it really belongs in a museum" said Mr. Morris, still not entirely relaxed about the whole series of events.

"Nonsense" replied the Fossil Man, angry about the unscrupulous way some 'experts' (who should know better) went about their business. "It belongs to you and only you can decide what to do with it, when you are good and ready."

Mr Morris read out a list of eight people who had been in contact.

"Jealous...harmless...nutcase...untrustworthy...waste of time...ok but irrelevant...nosy...mad as a box of frogs" came the Fossil Man's respective verdicts. "If you think they're bad I was also approached by a news reporter called 'Column' Carter who wanted all the details of the story for an exclusive 'scoop.' As he was talking to me I couldn't help noticing the snotty dew drop hanging from his nose, the persistent strand of saliva joining both of his lips, the grubby bitten down nails on his sweaty fingers and the remains of a vegetable curry on his moth-eaten shirt. There was something about him I didn't like."

As he put the phone down Mr. Morris couldn't help wondering why the science of palaeontology attracted such oddball characters, none of whom seemed to get on.

Some weeks later Daisy, her family and the Fossil Man took the small bones to Professor William Miller at a nearby university. His nickname was Dr. Bones on account of his staggering ability to correctly identify any animal in the world just by looking at one of its backbones, providing of course that it had some in the first place. Dr. Bones was one of the very best academics who studied these vertebrates. In fact he had written no fewer than two hundred learned articles about them. One thing Daisy noticed though, was that he used unusually long words to describe them.

"Goodness me!" the Professor yelped with obvious delight upon seeing the fossil for the first time.

He examined it carefully before offering an opinion. "It is evidently the fragmentary pelvic girdle belonging to a small adult female pterosaur from the Lower Cretaceous Period with a wingspan of approximately 75 cm. One can quite clearly see the adjacent vertebrae lying in complete articulation in the surrounding matrix. This creature perished 125 million years ago."

A puzzled Daisy turned to her father for clarification.

"It's a dead pterodactyl squashed into a lump of old mud," he told her.

Despite Miller's propensity to use ten gallon words, Daisy realised what this meant. She was sad to think that her pterosaur was once a living, breathing creature and that therefore it had ultimately died.

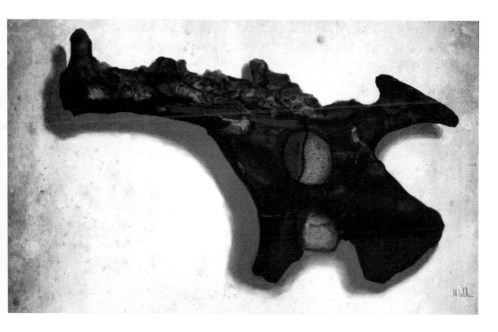

The pelvis and backbones of Daisy's fossil pterosaur

Noticing the tear welling up in her eye, the Professor's tone changed subtly as he made a conscious effort to communicate on a child's level.

"My dear girl" he said, choosing his words carefully, "because of the preservation of these fossilised bones, I can assure you that this magnificent little creature had a long life and went to rest in a peaceful manner."

Daisy looked suitably reassured.

"I think she'd have been content with that, don't you Daisy?"

"After all, it is not how one dies that really matters, it is how one LIVES."

These words of wisdom comforted the five-year old, who marvelled once again at her assemblage of small, shiny black bones.

"Just think Daisy," added the Fossil Man, "you were the very first person to see this pterosaur for 125 million years."

"And I was the second," chipped in her mother.

Not to be outdone Lily, Poppy and Riann had their turn.

"I was the third!"

"Fourth!"

"Fifth!"

There was a short pause.

"Seventeenth!" said Professor Miller, out-trumping them all.

Without knowing it at the time, Daisy Morris, a schoolgirl from the Isle of Wight, had discovered the partial remains of a rare pterosaur from the Lower Cretaceous Period, so rare in fact that it was completely 'new' to the scientific world. All those years ago the little reptile had embarked on a final epic journey, the journey of her lifetime. It ended somehow in a shallow lagoon in the soft muddy sediment that millions of years later would be hardened into the blue slipper clay. Her brittle white bones were buried quickly but would turn slowly into black mineralised fossils over countless millennia, entombed in thick layers of rock and eventually pushed up above sea level thanks to countless earthquakes. Finally the bones tumbled out of the cliff on the Isle of Wight ready to be washed by the winter waves, cleaned as perfectly as by any museum technician. Without doubt they would simply have been destroyed by the next tide had it not been for the fact that on that particular day at that particular place, the Morris family had chosen to go fossil collecting.

50 mm

Vectidraco: the scientist's interpretation (Darren Naish)

Chapter 9: The beginning of the end

A year later the summer on the Isle of Wight was one of the best for ages. The days were sunny and warm thanks to the arrival of a heat wave that was seven years overdue.

Daisy lent her pterosaur to the Fossil Man's temporary exhibition, where it took pride of place in a special glass cabinet. After all, she liked his museum best; it was real, dusty and genuine, just like her own private collection. Most of all she could see that the Fossil Man himself was part of the museum.

The fine weather meant the Island enjoyed a bumper tourist season, with many visitors flocking to see the new 'dinosaur' they had seen on the television or read about in the national newspapers.

The Morris family eventually decided to donate their fossil to the Natural History Museum in London, where it would be safely housed with the other 57 million-odd specimens. Here it would be made available to any bona fide researcher who cared to examine prehistoric reptiles. The family took a special day trip away from their little Island to visit London in the half term holidays, taking in a tour of the different animal galleries on offer. Daisy was mesmerised by the vast building with its countless rows of display cases full of skeletons, skulls and preserved carcasses. In the mammal hall the blue whale seemed as big as her village. The museum was like an iceberg, with most of the specimens hidden from public view in vast monotonous rows of locked cabinets. As it happened, her unique pterosaur would be kept in the same set of drawers that boasted the very first British example found by Miss Mary Anning all those years ago.

Fossil gargoyles adorning the outside of the Natural History Museum look down at three million visitors per year (RB)

The Lost Wight: Sometimes Daisy wished she could go back in time to the Age of Reptiles, but then again sometimes she didn't

In due course Professor Miller named the creature *Vectidraco daisymorrisae*, which in scientific language meant 'Daisy Morris's Isle of Wight dragon.' Despite being a pterosaur, however, everyone still referred to it as Daisy's Dinosaur. But like the hairy headmaster said, you shouldn't believe everything you read in the papers.

Dr. Shuban moved back to a museum in his native Romania to embark on a twenty year project cataloguing a collection of fossilised snails, while Mark Sciopi ended up in a fast food outlet in Portsmouth selling fried chicken nuggets and skinny latté. Carter opened a beauty salon in Leamington Spa.

Daisy herself continued to collect both real and fossilised bones, not just on the Isle of Wight but all over the world. Inspired by her pterosaur discovery, she became a professional palaeontologist and went on to write several scientific articles in her own right.

She embarked on many expeditions to various far flung places, and even went off in search of the Loch Ness Monster, alas that time with no success but still enjoying the experience nevertheless.

As for the Fossil Man, he too realised his main ambition, as the publicity surrounding Daisy's discovery resulted in enough sponsors coming forward to finance a permanent museum. Finally he could house his vast collection near the dinosaur beach and live in a home that didn't have piles of mammoth thigh bones in the bathroom.

Daisy's Epilogue: Making sense of it all

So there you have it, the story of my childhood discovery. If you followed the thread in your first reading and understood who said what to whom, well done, you did better than the Fossil Man (and he wrote it!).

Although I found many fossils in my lifetime (see page 44), it was the tiny pterosaur that would always have a special place in my life. Often I would imagine what it would be like to be living in the Age of Reptiles all those millions of years ago, flying freely like Ginky, my beloved Island dragon, without a care in the world.

Fin

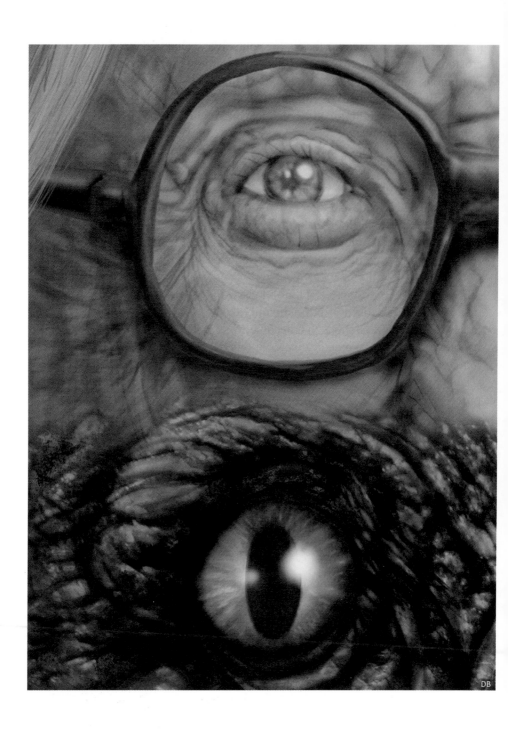

Finding Isle of Wight Fossils

The Isle of Wight is now known as Dinosaur Island and it is an excellent place to come and discover fossils for yourselves. Due to the constant erosion of the coastal cliffs, easily accessible at low tides, there is a continuous supply of specimens and good finds are surprisingly frequent, especially after storms. The following section is a brief guide to some of the best locations and typical fossils for which the Isle of Wight has become world famous.

What is a fossil?

Fossils are the remains of any animals or plants which have become buried in the sediment and then preserved in rock for more than 100,000 years or so. Palaeontology is the study of fossils (paleontology in the USA) and a palaeontologist is someone who studies them. Coprolites are fossil droppings and there is a word for someone who studies those, but I can't think of it at the moment.

Sometimes there is a lot of guesswork involved in palaeontology because it is normally only the hard parts such as the bones, teeth, claws or shells that become fossilised. A fossil species can be known by very fragmentary material or even by a single specimen, as in the case of _Vectidraco_. Colour itself does not fossilise, so a lot of the reconstructions you see in dinosaur books are only personal opinions or preferences. When I was a schoolboy most dinosaurs were brown, grey or green, and dragged their tails along the ground. However, the animal reconstructions change rapidly as new information is discovered. For example, compare the previous picture of the hatchling of _Vectidraco_ in this book with the one below depicting a soft, leathery eggshell. Thanks to recent discoveries we now know that many dinosaurs actually had feathers, an idea that would have been considered ridiculous fifty years ago.

Brief guide to fossils

Obviously, dinosaurs hog the limelight on the Isle of Wight. It is not unusual to go beachcombing on the southern coast and find the odd fragment of bone, vertebra (backbone) or even a tooth. Whole skeletons fall out of the crumbling cliffs every ten years or so on average, so there is more chance of finding a dinosaur here than of winning the lottery. The bones fall into the beach shingle, a pile of boulders washed over by the strong tides twice a day, and eventually they break up and are ground down into 'dino-pebbles.' Once you get your eye in, it is easy to recognise pieces of fossilised bone with their distinctive honey-comb pattern (like a crunchy bar). Most of them are now transformed into a black phosphatic material with an infilling of calcite or pyrite (fool's gold).

Apart from dinosaurs, you can occasionally find pieces of pterosaurs, turtles, crocodiles, fish, ichthyosaurs and even mammals. Some of the most impressive fossils to my mind are the giant, spirally coiled shells that used to be inhabited by sea creatures called ammonites, which come in a variety of shapes and sizes, occasionally up to the diameter of a car tyre. The down side is that they can weigh up to 75kg! The Island therefore has a set of strata from 125 million years ago to the present day with not much missing, so you have a range of fossil creatures from the Age of Reptiles right through to the Ice Age and beyond.

Best locations

The south side of the Island is old while the north side is relatively young, a situation caused by the fact that the strata have been previously tilted and then eroded into their present formations. The Chalk with its bands of flint forms a continuous 'backbone' and is well exposed at both sides, at Compton and Sandown Bays.

Alum Bay and the Needles

This is a must-see site because of the vertical coloured sands and fossil rich clays and limestones (snails and bivalves, fossil wood,) best viewed from the boat trips run from the beach.

Colwell and Totland Bays

The soft layers here contain a myriad of fossil shells which, despite being 40 million years old, are still 'shelly' and delicate. Occasional shark teeth are found too.

Cowes E. Cowes

Fishbourne

Yarmouth

Seaview

Ryde

Bem-
bridge

Newport

Brading

...ater

Brighstone Shorwell

Sandown

Godshill

Chale
Niton Ventnor

Shanklin

...therfield

Chale

to
Newport

The
Undercliff

...aale
...ine

Blackgang

to
Ventnor

Niton

...ale Bay

Rocken
End

St
Catherine's
Point

Besley

Yarmouth and Hamstead

This stretch of coast, best approached on a falling tide, is famous for its fragments of fossil turtle shell and the odd crocodile backbone or mammal molar, from a time long after the demise of the dinosaur.

Compton and Brook Bays

Here on a low tide you can see the famous Fossil Forest, a set of petrified tree sections dumped in an ancient delta, and you can even stand in the fossilised footprints made by plant eating dinosaurs called Iguanodon. Fossil wood covered in crystals of fool's gold is easy to find.

Shepherd's Chine to Whale Chine

Follow the route used by the Morris family and then turn eastwards, and you will see the alternating layers of shales, clays and sandstones full of bivalves, corals, ammonites and also fossil lobsters near Atherfield Point. Around Whale Chine you may be lucky enough to find a giant ammonite, usually hidden in enormous ironstone nodules which fell from the high cliffs and are now exposed at low water.

Yaverland

Here you can walk towards the Chalk cliffs and look for fossil shells in the limestone slabs above the high tide mark between the car park and Redcliff. Good hunting!

Glossary:

Ammonite	extinct mollusc, a squid in a spirally coiled shell
Cretaceous	a period of time after the Jurassic, from 145-65 million years ago
Dinosaurs	'fearfully great lizards'
Emanate	a posh ammonite
Genus	a group of species
Ginkgo	a fossil plant which still lives today
Heteromorph	unusually shaped ammonite
Ichthyosaur	'fish lizard,' a marine reptile
Jurassic	a period of time from 200-145 million years ago
Mosasaur	'Meuse lizard,' originally found in Holland, a marine reptile
Nessie	the Loch Ness Monster, which does not exist (or does it?)
Plesiosaur	a long necked marine reptile
Pliosaur	a shorter necked plesiosaur
Pterodactylus	one specific type of pterosaur
Pterosaur	'winged lizards'